KU-471-457

This edition copyright © Robert Frederick Ltd.
Downwood, Claverton Down Road, Bath BA2 6DT

First published 1993
Al rights reserved.

Acknowledgements
Typesetting: Creative Design & Typesetting
Reproduction in Hong Kong
Printed in the UK

Address Book

with 13 colour plates

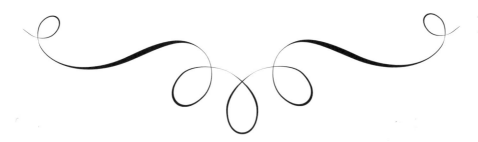

A

Name	Telephone
Address	

Name	Telephone
Address	

Name	Telephone
Address	

Name	Telephone
Address	

Name	Telephone
Address	

Name	Telephone
Address	

Name	Telephone
Address	

Name	Telephone
Address	

Name	Telephone
Address	

Name	Telephone
Address	

A

| Name | Telephone |
| Address | |

| Name | Telephone |
| Address | |

| Name | Telephone |
| Address | |

| Name | Telephone |
| Address | |

| Name | Telephone |
| Address | |

| Name | Telephone |
| Address | |

| Name | Telephone |
| Address | |

| Name | Telephone |
| Address | |

| Name | Telephone |
| Address | |

| Name | Telephone |
| Address | |

"A friend may well be reckoned the masterpiece of nature."

Ralph Waldo Emerson

Name   Telephone

Address

Name   Telephone

Address

Name   Telephone

Address

Name   Telephone

Address

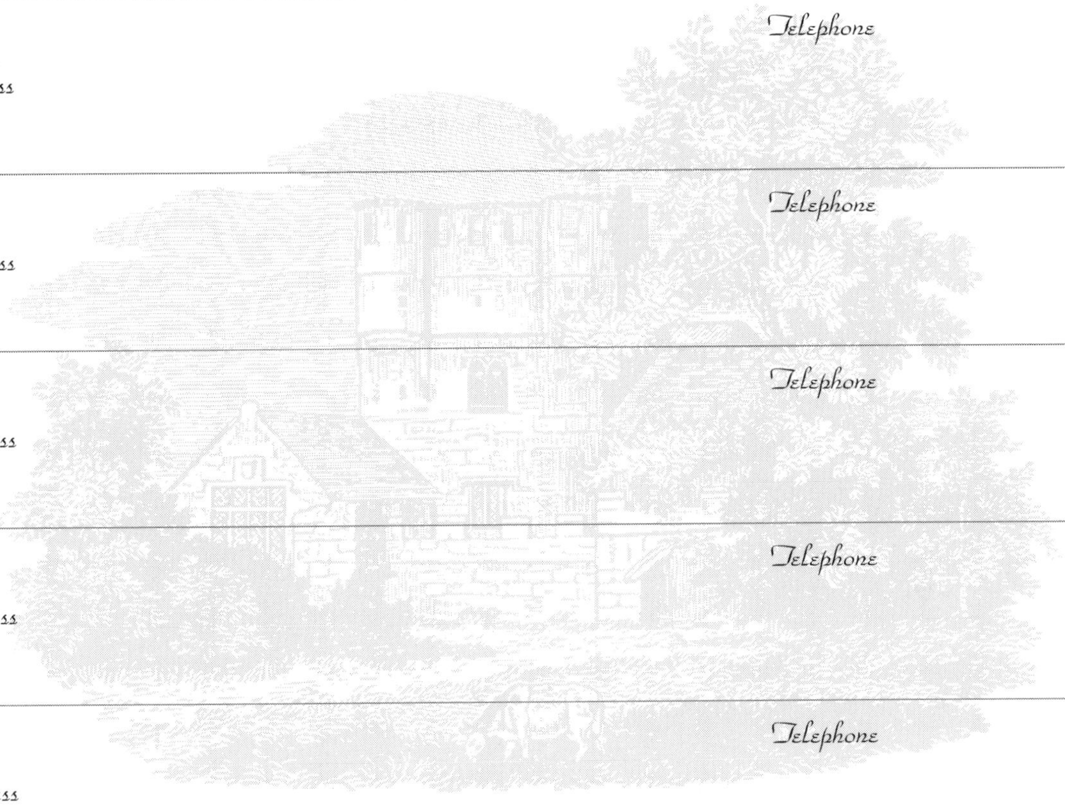

Name   Telephone

Address

Name   Telephone

Address

Name   Telephone

Address

Name   Telephone

Address

Name   Telephone

Address

Name   Telephone

Address

"A friend is a gift you give yourself."

Robert Louis Stevenson

B

Name	Telephone
Address	

Name	Telephone
Address	

Name	Telephone
Address	

Name	Telephone
Address	

Name	Telephone
Address	

Name	Telephone
Address	

Name	Telephone
Address	

Name	Telephone
Address	

Name	Telephone
Address	

Name	Telephone
Address	

C

Name	Telephone
Address	

Name	Telephone
Address	

Name	Telephone
Address	

Name	Telephone
Address	

Name	Telephone
Address	

Name	Telephone
Address	

Name	Telephone
Address	

Name	Telephone
Address	

Name	Telephone
Address	

Name	Telephone
Address	

"Children are the true connoisseurs. What's precious to them has no price, only value."

Bel Kaufman

C

Name	*Telephone*
Address	

Name	*Telephone*
Address	

Name	*Telephone*
Address	

Name	*Telephone*
Address	

Name	*Telephone*
Address	

Name	*Telephone*
Address	

Name	*Telephone*
Address	

Name	*Telephone*
Address	

Name	*Telephone*
Address	

Name	*Telephone*
Address	

"Success generally depends upon knowing how long it takes to succeed."

C. L. De Montesquieu

D

Name	Telephone
Address	

Name	Telephone
Address	

Name	Telephone
Address	

Name	Telephone
Address	

Name	Telephone
Address	

Name	Telephone
Address	

Name	Telephone
Address	

Name	Telephone
Address	

Name	Telephone
Address	

Name	Telephone
Address	

D

Name	Telephone
Address	

Name	Telephone
Address	

Name	Telephone
Address	

Name	Telephone
Address	

Name	Telephone
Address	

Name	Telephone
Address	

Name	Telephone
Address	

Name	Telephone
Address	

Name	Telephone
Address	

Name	Telephone
Address	

"Don't be afraid to take big steps. You can't cross a chasm in two small jumps."

David Lloyd George

E

Name | Telephone
Address

Name | Telephone
Address

Name | Telephone
Address

Name | Telephone
Address

Name | Telephone
Address

Name | Telephone
Address

Name | Telephone
Address

Name | Telephone
Address

Name | Telephone
Address

Name | Telephone
Address

"What matters is not the size of the dog in the fight, but the size of the fight in the dog."

Coach Bear Bryant

E

Name	Telephone
Address	

Name	Telephone
Address	

Name	Telephone
Address	

Name	Telephone
Address	

Name	Telephone
Address	

Name	Telephone
Address	

Name	Telephone
Address	

Name	Telephone
Address	

Name	Telephone
Address	

Name	Telephone
Address	

F

Name	*Telephone*
Address	

Name	*Telephone*
Address	

Name	*Telephone*
Address	

Name	*Telephone*
Address	

Name	*Telephone*
Address	

Name	*Telephone*
Address	

Name	*Telephone*
Address	

Name	*Telephone*
Address	

Name	*Telephone*
Address	

Name	*Telephone*
Address	

"Parting is all we know of heaven / And all we need of hell."

Emily Dickinson

F

Name	*Telephone*
Address	

Name	*Telephone*
Address	

Name	*Telephone*
Address	

Name	*Telephone*
Address	

Name	*Telephone*
Address	

Name	*Telephone*
Address	

Name	*Telephone*
Address	

Name	*Telephone*
Address	

Name	*Telephone*
Address	

Name	*Telephone*
Address	

"A smooth sea never made a skillful mariner."
English Proverb

G

Name   *Telephone*

Address

Name   *Telephone*

Address

Name   *Telephone*

Address

Name   *Telephone*

Address

Name   *Telephone*

Address

Name   *Telephone*

Address

Name   *Telephone*

Address

Name   *Telephone*

Address

Name   *Telephone*

Address

Name   *Telephone*

Address

G

Name	*Telephone*
Address	

Name	*Telephone*
Address	

Name	*Telephone*
Address	

Name	*Telephone*
Address	

Name	*Telephone*
Address	

Name	*Telephone*
Address	

Name	*Telephone*
Address	

Name	*Telephone*
Address	

Name	*Telephone*
Address	

Name	*Telephone*
Address	

"A true friend is the greatest of all blessings."

La Rochefoucauld

H

Name   Telephone

Address

Name   Telephone

Address

Name   Telephone

Address

Name   Telephone

Address

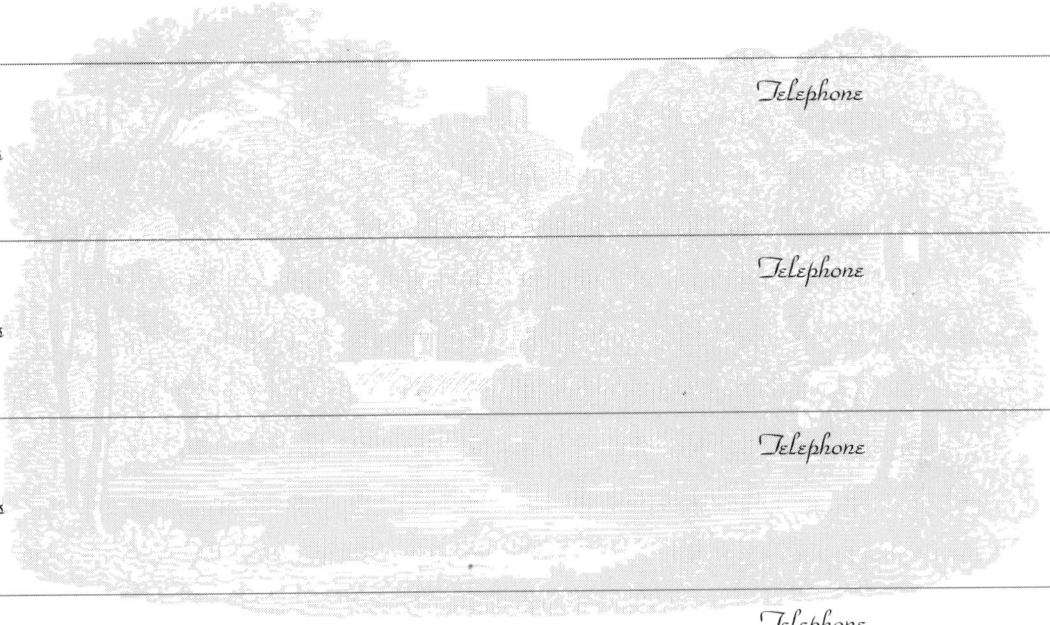

Name   Telephone

Address

Name   Telephone

Address

Name   Telephone

Address

Name   Telephone

Address

Name   Telephone

Address

Name   Telephone

Address

"Happiness makes up in height for what it lacks in length."

Robert Frost

H

Name	Telephone
Address	

Name	Telephone
Address	

Name	Telephone
Address	

Name	Telephone
Address	

Name	Telephone
Address	

Name	Telephone
Address	

Name	Telephone
Address	

Name	Telephone
Address	

Name	Telephone
Address	

Name	Telephone
Address	

I

| Name | Telephone |
| Address | |

| Name | Telephone |
| Address | |

| Name | Telephone |
| Address | |

| Name | Telephone |
| Address | |

| Name | Telephone |
| Address | |

| Name | Telephone |
| Address | |

| Name | Telephone |
| Address | |

| Name | Telephone |
| Address | |

| Name | Telephone |
| Address | |

| Name | Telephone |
| Address | |

"There is no home that is not twice as beautiful as the most beautiful city."

West African Proverb

J

Name	Telephone
Address	

Name	Telephone
Address	

Name	Telephone
Address	

Name	Telephone
Address	

Name	Telephone
Address	

Name	Telephone
Address	

Name	Telephone
Address	

Name	Telephone
Address	

Name	Telephone
Address	

Name	Telephone
Address	

"There's nothing worth the wear of winning, / But laughter and the love of friends."

Hilaire Belloc

J

| Name | Telephone |
| Address | |

| Name | Telephone |
| Address | |

| Name | Telephone |
| Address | |

| Name | Telephone |
| Address | |

| Name | Telephone |
| Address | |

| Name | Telephone |
| Address | |

| Name | Telephone |
| Address | |

| Name | Telephone |
| Address | |

| Name | Telephone |
| Address | |

| Name | Telephone |
| Address | |

K

Name	*Telephone*
Address	

Name	*Telephone*
Address	

Name	*Telephone*
Address	

Name	*Telephone*
Address	

Name	*Telephone*
Address	

Name	*Telephone*
Address	

Name	*Telephone*
Address	

Name	*Telephone*
Address	

Name	*Telephone*
Address	

Name	*Telephone*
Address	

"Trees and fields tell me nothing; men are my teachers."

Plato

L

Name		Telephone
Address		

Name		Telephone
Address		

Name		Telephone
Address		

Name		Telephone
Address		

Name		Telephone
Address		

Name		Telephone
Address		

Name		Telephone
Address		

Name		Telephone
Address		

Name		Telephone
Address		

Name		Telephone
Address		

"What is this life if, full of care, / We have no time to stand and stare?"

W H Davies

L

Name	*Telephone*
Address	

Name	*Telephone*
Address	

Name	*Telephone*
Address	

Name	*Telephone*
Address	

Name	*Telephone*
Address	

Name	*Telephone*
Address	

Name	*Telephone*
Address	

Name	*Telephone*
Address	

Name	*Telephone*
Address	

Name	*Telephone*
Address	

M

Name	Telephone
Address	

Name	Telephone
Address	

Name	Telephone
Address	

Name	Telephone
Address	

Name	Telephone
Address	

Name	Telephone
Address	

Name	Telephone
Address	

Name	Telephone
Address	

Name	Telephone
Address	

Name	Telephone
Address	

"Laughter has no foreign accent."

Paul Lowney

M

Name	*Telephone*
Address	

Name	*Telephone*
Address	

Name	*Telephone*
Address	

Name	*Telephone*
Address	

Name	*Telephone*
Address	

Name	*Telephone*
Address	

Name	*Telephone*
Address	

Name	*Telephone*
Address	

Name	*Telephone*
Address	

Name	*Telephone*
Address	

"To the art of working well a civilised race would add the art of playing well."

George Santayana

N

Name	Telephone
Address	

Name	Telephone
Address	

Name	Telephone
Address	

Name	Telephone
Address	

Name	Telephone
Address	

Name	Telephone
Address	

Name	Telephone
Address	

Name	Telephone
Address	

Name	Telephone
Address	

Name	Telephone
Address	

N

Name	Telephone
Address	

Name	Telephone
Address	

Name	Telephone
Address	

Name	Telephone
Address	

Name	Telephone
Address	

Name	Telephone
Address	

Name	Telephone
Address	

Name	Telephone
Address	

Name	Telephone
Address	

Name	Telephone
Address	

"Love is an act of endless forgiveness, a tender look which becomes a habit."

Peter Ustinov

O

Name	*Telephone*
Address	

Name	*Telephone*
Address	

Name	*Telephone*
Address	

Name	*Telephone*
Address	

Name	*Telephone*
Address	

Name	*Telephone*
Address	

Name	*Telephone*
Address	

Name	*Telephone*
Address	

Name	*Telephone*
Address	

Name	*Telephone*
Address	

"Bliss in possession will not last; / Remembered joys are never past."

James Montgomery

O

Name	*Telephone*
Address	

Name	*Telephone*
Address	

Name	*Telephone*
Address	

Name	*Telephone*
Address	

Name	*Telephone*
Address	

Name	*Telephone*
Address	

Name	*Telephone*
Address	

Name	*Telephone*
Address	

Name	*Telephone*
Address	

Name	*Telephone*
Address	

P

Name   Telephone

Address

Name   Telephone

Address

Name   Telephone

Address

Name   Telephone

Address

Name   Telephone

Address

Name   Telephone

Address

Name   Telephone

Address

Name   Telephone

Address

Name   Telephone

Address

Name   Telephone

Address

"The love we give away is the only love we keep."

Elbert Hubbard

P

| Name | Telephone |
| Address | |

| Name | Telephone |
| Address | |

| Name | Telephone |
| Address | |

| Name | Telephone |
| Address | |

| Name | Telephone |
| Address | |

| Name | Telephone |
| Address | |

| Name | Telephone |
| Address | |

| Name | Telephone |
| Address | |

| Name | Telephone |
| Address | |

| Name | Telephone |
| Address | |

"God gave us memories that we might have roses in December."

James M Barrie

Q

Name	Telephone
Address	

Name	Telephone
Address	

Name	Telephone
Address	

Name	Telephone
Address	

Name	Telephone
Address	

Name	Telephone
Address	

Name	Telephone
Address	

Name	Telephone
Address	

Name	Telephone
Address	

Name	Telephone
Address	

R

Name	Telephone
Address	

Name	Telephone
Address	

Name	Telephone
Address	

Name	Telephone
Address	

Name	Telephone
Address	

Name	Telephone
Address	

Name	Telephone
Address	

Name	Telephone
Address	

Name	Telephone
Address	

Name	Telephone
Address	

"To be able to enjoy one's past life is to live twice."

Martial

R

Name   Telephone
Address

Name   Telephone
Address

Name   Telephone
Address

Name   Telephone
Address

Name   Telephone
Address

Name   Telephone
Address

Name   Telephone
Address

Name   Telephone
Address

Name   Telephone
Address

Name   Telephone
Address

"Who hears music feels his solitude / Peopled at once."
Robert Browning

S

Name	*Telephone*
Address	

Name	*Telephone*
Address	

Name	*Telephone*
Address	

Name	*Telephone*
Address	

Name	*Telephone*
Address	

Name	*Telephone*
Address	

Name	*Telephone*
Address	

Name	*Telephone*
Address	

Name	*Telephone*
Address	

Name	*Telephone*
Address	

S

Name	Telephone
Address	

Name	Telephone
Address	

Name	Telephone
Address	

Name	Telephone
Address	

Name	Telephone
Address	

Name	Telephone
Address	

Name	Telephone
Address	

Name	Telephone
Address	

Name	Telephone
Address	

Name	Telephone
Address	

"The return makes one love the farewell."

Alfred de Musset

T

Name	Telephone
Address	

Name	Telephone
Address	

Name	Telephone
Address	

Name	Telephone
Address	

Name	Telephone
Address	

Name	Telephone
Address	

Name	Telephone
Address	

Name	Telephone
Address	

Name	Telephone
Address	

Name	Telephone
Address	

"Good company and good discourse are the very sinews of virtue."

Izaak Walton

T

Name   Telephone

Address

Name   Telephone

Address

Name   Telephone

Address

Name   Telephone

Address

Name   Telephone

Address

Name   Telephone

Address

Name   Telephone

Address

Name   Telephone

Address

Name   Telephone

Address

Name   Telephone

Address

U

Name   Telephone

Address

Name   Telephone

Address

Name   Telephone

Address

Name   Telephone

Address

Name   Telephone

Address

Name   Telephone

Address

Name   Telephone

Address

Name   Telephone

Address

Name   Telephone

Address

Name   Telephone

Address

U

Name	Telephone
Address	

Name	Telephone
Address	

Name	Telephone
Address	

Name	Telephone
Address	

Name	Telephone
Address	

Name	Telephone
Address	

Name	Telephone
Address	

Name	Telephone
Address	

Name	Telephone
Address	

Name	Telephone
Address	

"You must never 'find' time for anything. If you want time you must make it."

Charles Buxton

V

Name	*Telephone*
Address	

Name	*Telephone*
Address	

Name	*Telephone*
Address	

Name	*Telephone*
Address	

Name	*Telephone*
Address	

Name	*Telephone*
Address	

Name	*Telephone*
Address	

Name	*Telephone*
Address	

Name	*Telephone*
Address	

Name	*Telephone*
Address	

"An agreeable companion on a journey is as good as a carriage."

Publilius Syrus

W

Name   Telephone

Address

Name   Telephone

Address

Name   Telephone

Address

Name   Telephone

Address

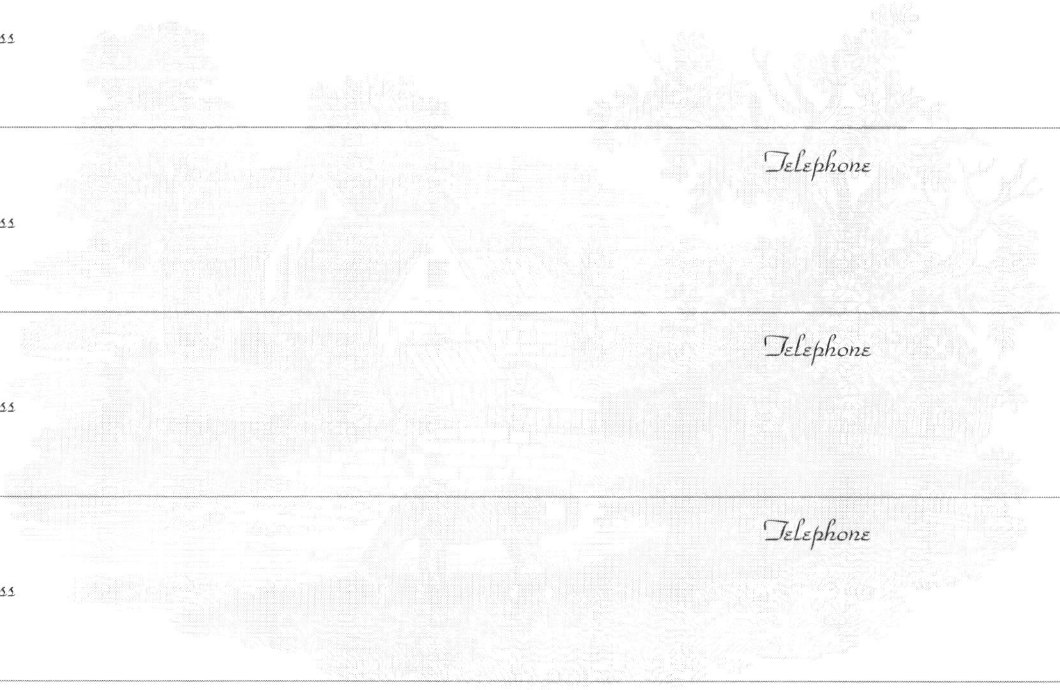

Name   Telephone

Address

Name   Telephone

Address

Name   Telephone

Address

Name   Telephone

Address

Name   Telephone

Address

Name   Telephone

Address

XYZ

Name   Telephone

Address

Name   Telephone

Address

Name   Telephone

Address

Name   Telephone

Address

Name   Telephone

Address

Name   Telephone

Address

Name   Telephone

Address

Name   Telephone

Address

Name   Telephone

Address

Name   Telephone

Address

X, Y, Z

Name   *Telephone*
Address

Name   *Telephone*
Address

Name   *Telephone*
Address

Name   *Telephone*
Address

Name   *Telephone*
Address

Name   *Telephone*
Address

Name   *Telephone*
Address

Name   *Telephone*
Address

Name   *Telephone*
Address

Name   *Telephone*
Address

"Not vain the weakest, if their force unite."

Homer: Iliad

MISC

Name   Telephone
Address

Name   Telephone
Address

Name   Telephone
Address

Name   Telephone
Address

Name   Telephone
Address

Name   Telephone
Address

Name   Telephone
Address

Name   Telephone
Address

Name   Telephone
Address

Name   Telephone
Address

"You are as welcome as the flowers in May."

Charles Macklin